Unicorn Jazz

OCEAN ANIMALS

Lisa Caprelli & Davey Villalobos

Ocean Animals

Teachers & Educators get free beyond this book
ACTIVITY PAGES at:

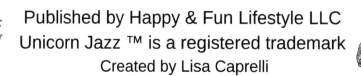

UnicornJazz.com

Published by Happy & Fun Lifestyle LLC
Unicorn Jazz ™ is a registered trademark
Created by Lisa Caprelli

Author: Lisa Caprelli
Illustrator: Davey Villalobos
Contributions by C. Herzig and Amanda Keaton

Acknowledgements: Amanda Keaton, Aisha Armer, Ruth Leigh, Alyssa Ruiz, Suzanne Funk, Shannon Anderson, Amanda Nunez, Natalia Sepulveda and our wonderful **Unicorn Jazz Community, Family & Friends**

Printed in USA - 1st Edition 2021
Library of Congress Control Number 2021901152
Publisher's Cataloging in Publication Data:
Author: Caprelli, Lisa; **Illustrator**: Villalobos, Davey
Title: **Ocean Animals**
Subtitle: Unicorn Jazz Unicorn Book Series
Series: **Unicorn Jazz**
Hardcover ISBN: 978-1-951203-18-4
Paperback ISBN: 978-1-951203-17-7
Kindle ISBN:978-1-951203-19-1

Resident comic
Live among anemone
STRIPES help to find me!

CLOWNFISH

Hard shell makes up reefs

Looks like plant but animal

Colony of Clones

CORAL

Playful with cute smiles
Splash, click-clickity noises:

EC-HO-LO-CA-TION

DOLPHIN

Clumsy on the land
Dominant bulls fight others

An
ELEPHANT nose

ELEPHANT SEAL

Floating in the waves

Beware of jelly stingers!

OUCH!

Hide your fingers

JELLYFISH

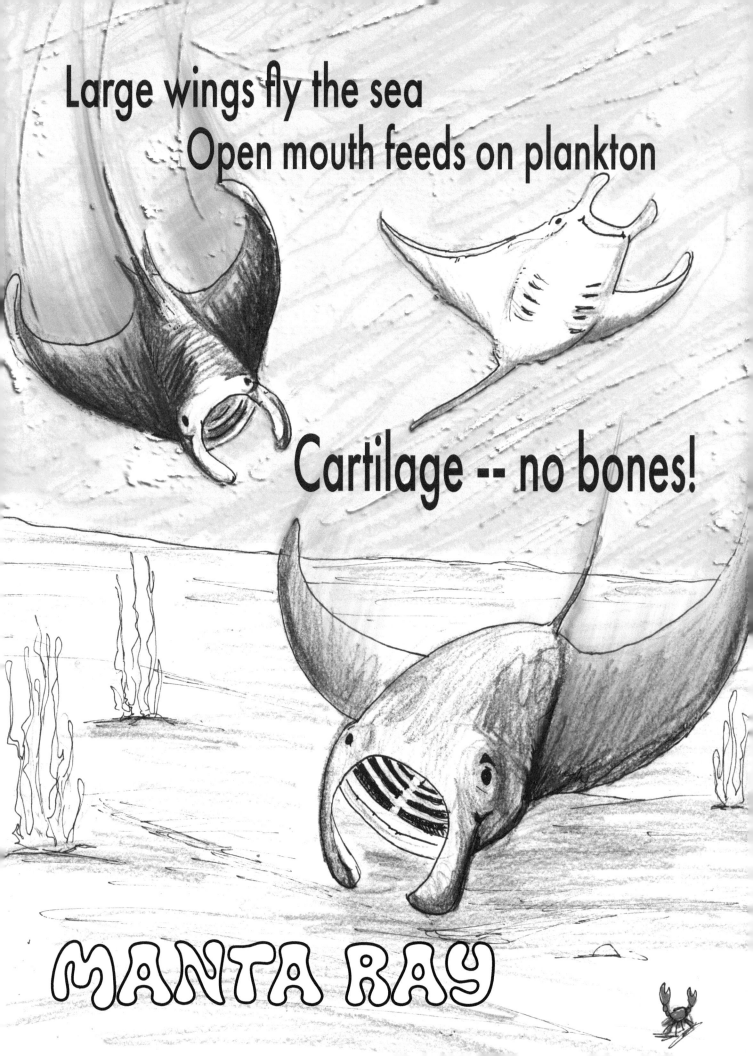

Large wings fly the sea
Open mouth feeds on plankton

Cartilage -- no bones!

MANTA RAY

BLACK and WHITE toothed whale

Eats fish, seals, walrus, and sharks!

Named **Wolves of the Sea**

WADDLE is our group

Antarctica! Ice is home

Birds with flippers swim

PENGUINS

Lives at the bottom

A safe shelter for Clownfish

Harpoon TENTACLES

SEA ANEMONE

Sway along the coast
With our tails linked together

Male pouch holds babies

SEAHORSE

GIANT fish, BIG teeth
Cartilage skeleton... *fast!*

Sharp sense of smell... BITE!

SHARK

Filter feed plankton

Thousands of holes hold water

Don't move... self-cleaning

SPONGE

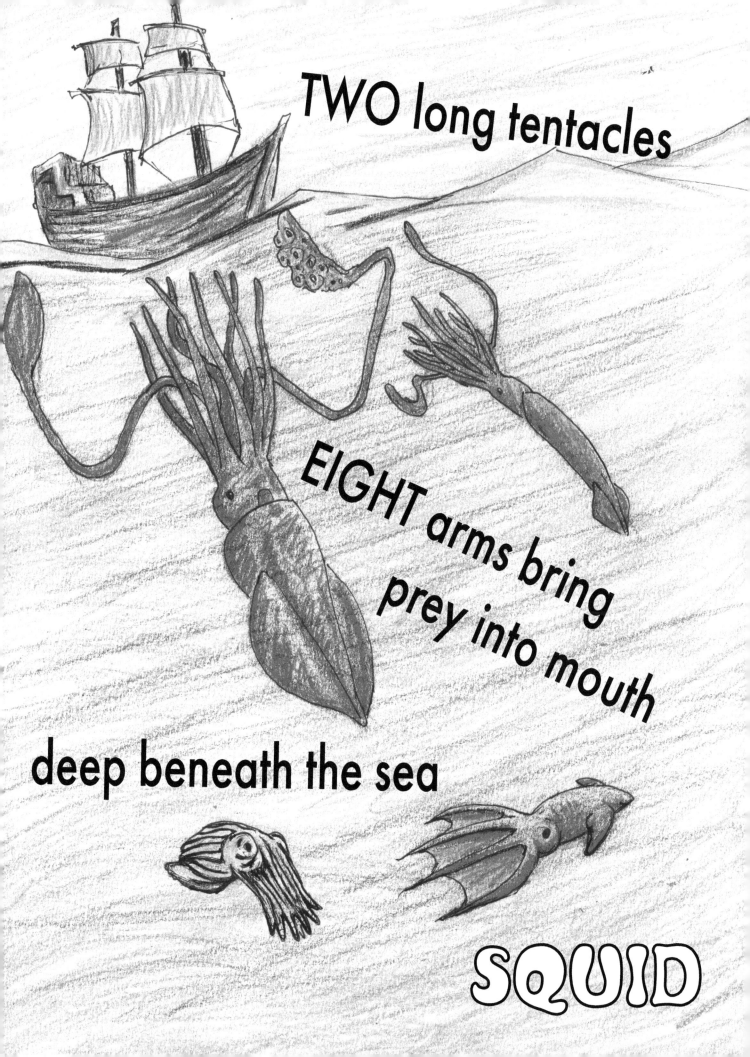

~ The End ~.

We see sea life love
Past glorious adventures
You are always here!

Ocean Animals
Teacher's Beyond the Book Learning Activities
UnicornJazz.com

...ean Animals by Lisa Caprelli & Davey Villalobos is a fun, colorful exploration of **sea life** ...d **poetry**. Young readers will learn about various underwater creatures through creative ...ku and beautiful illustrations. The Common Core State Standards encourage children to ...arn about poem structure, rhythm and patterns by Grade 4. Ocean Animals is a great ...source for teaching these concepts as well as other topics such as oceanography and ...arine biology.

The Ocean Animals activities were designed to meet learning standards (CCSS and NGSS) ...such as:

- Recognize common types of texts (e.g., storybooks, poems
- Explain major differences between poems, drama, and pro: elements of poems (e.g., verse, rhythm, meter)
- Describe how words and phrases (e.g., regular beats, allite lines) supply rhythm and meaning in a story, poem, or son
- Use illustrations and details in a story to describe its chara
- Use a model to represent the relationship between the ne animals and the places they live. Living things need water land, and they live in places that have the things they nee

Ocean Animal Vocabulary

You may have noticed more special words in the story. Here's a glossary to help you understand what they mean.

anemone - Sea anemones are marine animals that look like flowers. They have many sticky limbs called tentacles. Sea anemones use their tentacles to catch prey and stick to large rocks.

bioluminescent - Bioluminescent creatures can create light with their bodies. Some jellyfish and squid are bioluminescent.

camouflage - This is when animals blend in with the environment. It helps them hide from predators, or animals that hunt them for food.

decapod - Decapods are sea creatures that have 10 legs. Crabs, lobsters and shrimp are decapods.

echolocation - This is when animals use sounds to find things. Dolphins send sound waves through the water. They listen for the echo. This helps them find out where other animals are located.

exoskeleton - An exoskeleton is a special covering that protects an animal's body. Clams and oysters have an exoskeleton called a shell.

plankton - Plankton are tiny living things that float around the ocean. They are eaten by other sea creatures such as fish.

Did you notice any other **new or strange words in the story**? Use a dictionary to mean. Write the definitions below.

_____

_____

_____

_____

Ocean Prefixes, Suffixes and Root Words

Marine biology is the study of the ocean and the creatures that live in it. When you learn about sea life, you may hear special words. These words have prefixes, suffixes and root words that have important origins. They were used many years ago to describe the ocean languages like Greek or Latin. They were used many years ago to describe the ocean

- aqua- means "water"
- -mar- means "sea"
- sub- means "under"
- bio- means "life"
- -logy means "the study of"

Look at these words floating in the ocean. Circle the prefixes, suffixes and/or root words from the list above. Think about what these words mean. You can use a dictionary to check your guesses.

Marine
Submarine
Biology
Submerge
Aquatic
Aquarium

CPSIA information can be obtained
at www.ICGtesting.com
Printed in the USA
BVHW021529181121
621673BV00027B/486